DARK AGE SCULPTURE

KU-328-418

DARK AGE SCULPTURE

A selection from the collections of
the National Museum of Antiquities of Scotland.

Joanna Close-Brooks
and
Robert B K Stevenson

National Museum of Antiquities of Scotland
Edinburgh
Her Majesty's Stationery Office

© Crown copyright 1982
First published 1982
Second impression 1989
ISBN 0 11 492015 X

Illustrations
National Museum of Antiquities of Scotland, all pages except:
Royal Commission on the Ancient and Historical Monuments of Scotland,
pages 9 (right), 19, 20
Thames and Hudson Ltd, pages 21, 22
Scottish Development Department, pages 8, 10, 11, 36

CONTENTS

The National Museum catalogue number to each item (eg. IB 240) is given at the beginning of the description. References to publications are given at the end of each entry; see page 45 for explanation of the abbreviations.

INTRODUCTION

Sculptured Monuments in Scotland, AD 400–1100

The sculptured monuments of these centuries, weathered and broken, scattered in fields, churchyards and museums, are surprising in their number, their variety, and often their impact. Some of them are among the country's most notable artistic achievements, such as the crosses at Ruthwell and Iona and the Cadboll stone. These are products of the strange 'Golden Age' when the most splendid Gospel manuscripts were illuminated at Lindisfarne, near Berwick, and probably at Iona.

These stone monuments bring us into most direct contact with early times, but their exact purpose and full meaning is generally obscure. Different styles are found in different areas of Scotland as described in this booklet, and emphasise the different peoples and kingdoms known from the scanty historical records: Britons, Anglo-Saxons, Scots, Picts and (after 800) Norsemen. All dates suggested for the sculpture involve many uncertainties.

Most, perhaps all, the monuments reflect cultural links with the Roman world that were strengthened, after the end of the Roman Empire, by the spread of Christianity. Along with Bible figures, mythical beasts, symbolic vine-scrolls and plaited and meander patterns, we see Celtic curves and spirals related to the metalwork of before AD 200 and somehow revived. The Anglo-Saxons contributed interlaced creatures, and can be credited with a major part in fusing together all elements of art in the British Isles, particularly in Gospel manuscripts after 650. From this 'insular' amalgam local styles developed in the 8th century and continued to evolve, but wars and isolation, intensified by the Viking invasions, led to cultural decline from the 9th century onwards.

South

The Britons, living south of the Forth and Clyde, were related to the modern Welsh. Rare British tombstones of the 5th and 6th centuries AD were inscribed in Latin, sometimes with a simple cross or monogram of Christ (chi-rho). Soon after 600 the Britons lost the present regions of Lothian and Borders, and Dumfriesshire, to the Anglo-Saxons of Northumbria. The kingdom of Strathclyde, which remained British, lacked monuments until the 10th century: probably its arts were poetry and music.

In Anglo-Saxon Northumbria, Christianity was first successfully established by Irish missionaries from Iona (634–44) and in this

Ruthwell, Dumfriesshire.
Anglian Cross.

period the monumental cross in wood was invented. Then the Northumbrians turned to the Roman Church. Stones masons and sculptors were soon imported. The first and finest sculptured crosses, with most naturalistic sculpture, may however be little earlier than 750 (Hexham in Tyneside and Ruthwell in Dumfriesshire). Unlike medieval crosses, they are not crucifixes (with the dead Christ), but symbols of the risen Christ, and they may mark preaching places. There followed the cross-shafts from Aberlady, (p 16), Morham (p 17) and Hoddom (p 18). With later work they inspired the sculpture of the Picts and the Scots.

Beginning in 793 Scandinavian raids and colonisation resulted in very mixed populations with pagan traditions. The 10th and 11th century sculpture of Galloway and the Clyde reflects such mixtures (coffin and 'hog-back' tombstones at Govan, Glasgow; Glenluce cross-slab p 41).

West

In the territory of the Scots, who had colonised Argyll from Ireland, there was the monastery at Iona founded in 563 by St Columba. Towards 800 this monastery probably produced great manuscripts (the Book of Kells) and certainly experimented in constructing stone crosses. These sometimes had the ring or halo which became a feature of the 'high crosses' of Ireland (the cross at Kildalton, Islay, is part of the Iona group). The spiral patterns on these crosses were simplified from manuscripts, their high bosses and snakes from metalwork and probably from Pictish sculpture. The Vikings disrupted this creative centre. Much later the Pictish form of cross-slab, adopted in the Isle of Man, was used in the part-Norwegian isles (cross-slabs from Kilbar, Barra, with runic inscription, and from Islay, pp 43–44).

East and North

The Picts may have been a mixture of Britons and of people who retained an earlier, non-Celtic, language and customs. Columba and other missionaries converted them to Christianity and founded monasteries. By 710 they had conformed to the Roman Church. Their kingdom then stretched from the Forth to the far north and west, and was strong and centralised, the kings living near the Tay.

Symbol Stones

Unworked stones or slabs incised with a unique system of symbols are found throughout the Pictish area (map p 12). The earliest are probably late 7th century, the majority 8th century in date; but some, notably in Aberdeenshire, may be later still. Particularly well-designed stones, perhaps the earliest of all, are found round the Moray and Dornoch Firths. The meaning of the symbols is lost, but was perhaps social rather than religious. Rare accompanying inscriptions in ogam letters consist of, or include, personal names,

Newton, Aberdeenshire.
Symbol Stone.

Iona, Argyll. St. John's Cross
(replica) in the foreground,
St. Martin's Cross behind.

Glamis, Angus. Cross-slab.

Dupplin, Perthshire. Cross.

and some at least of the stones are probably tombstones. The commonest of the symbols are repeated nation-wide, and so are unlikely to have been restricted to a family or clan. Some symbols depict known things, such as animals, and a two-handed cauldron seen from above; others appear to be just geometrical shapes. Generally they are in pairs; an added mirror, and often comb, may indicate a woman. Symbols are occasionally found on the walls of caves or other natural rock faces. They are also incised on two heavy silver chains and on several minor objects, displayed in the National Museum.

Cross-slabs

When crosses sculptured in relief were introduced to Pictland after 750 it was in the remarkable form of a great page in stone, up to ten feet high (pp 29–33). Possibly this development first took place in Strathmore (Angus). The Cross was covered with interlace patterns, perhaps combining the ideas of the Cross and of the Vine as the Tree of Life. The Pictish symbols continued prominent, quickly transformed into relief but no longer alone; they were generally on the back of the cross-slab, where there was also figure sculpture in profile. The figures were derived from Biblical manuscripts and other imported works of art. The stone from Hilton of Cadboll, Ross-shire (p 32), apparently shows a Pictish lady hunting, but also trumpeters from an illustration of David the Psalmist.

The Norsemen overran the northern isles before these developments got far, and no typical cross-slabs with symbols are known from the area. The Brough of Birsay stone from Orkney has warriors but incised symbols; its cross-face is lost. The only symbol on the cross-slab from Papil, Shetland, is the lion of St Mark.

Relief became high and fully rounded only for a short time early in the 9th century, notably on the tomb-shrine at St Andrews; its David scenes and snakelike intertwined animals and bosses covered with low relief are related to Iona sculpture. Some free-standing crosses and other types of monuments were set up in the East, particularly after the Scots took over the Pictish kingdom about 843 (Dupplin cross). The symbols then diminished and disappeared, after a brief extra-prominence round the Moray Firth. The stones generally got smaller, with cruder figures often front-facing (Invergowrie cross-slab, p 39). Irish and Scandinavian influences appeared. Finally sculpture embellished doorways, as at the 11th century round-tower of Brechin, Angus and on the arch from Forteviot, Perthshire (p 40), now the entrance to the National Museum's sculpture display.

Inscriptions

After the Latin inscriptions on 5th–6th century British tombstones, lettering in rather simple Roman capitals only recurs on the Ruthwell cross of the mid 8th century, to identify the Biblical figures.

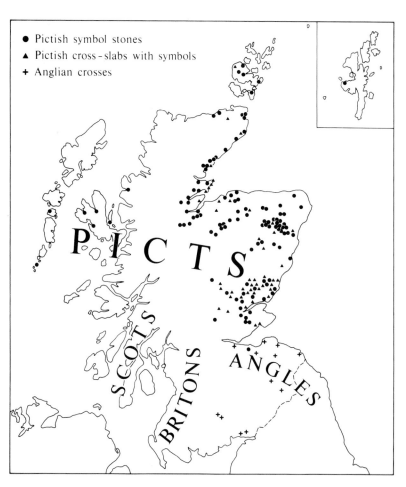

Map of places where Pictish stones with symbols and Anglian crosses have been found in Scotland.

Legend on map:
● Pictish symbol stones
▲ Pictish cross-slabs with symbols
+ Anglian crosses

PICTS

SCOTS

BRITONS

ANGLES

That cross is also unique in having Anglo-Saxon religious poetry (the Dream of the Rood) carved on it; the longest known inscription in Anglo-Saxon runes.

A modified form of the Irish ogam letter-cipher is found both on the symbol stones of the Picts and on their cross-slabs, in the 8th and 9th centuries; a late ogam inscription from Bressay, Shetland includes the Norse word for daughter (p 35).

Two fragmentary inscriptions in ornamental capital letters associated with spiral designs show what the lost monastic manuscripts of Pictland looked like (Tarbat, Ross-shire, and Lethnott, Angus). Three names in the 'miniscule' lettering of the manuscripts are inscribed on the edge of a cross at St Vigeans, Angus.

Scandinavian runes were introduced by the Vikings. The earliest such runic inscriptions in Scotland are gravestones of the 10th and 11th centuries AD (cross-slab from Kilbar, Barra, p 43). Later runic inscriptions include those incised on the walls of the neolithic chambered tomb of Maes Howe on Orkney, some of which may relate to the expedition of Earl Rognald to the Holy Land in 1150–1.

EARLY CHRISTIAN GRAVESTONES

In Scotland, gravestones of the early centuries AD are found only in Galloway, Lothian and the Borders. These gravestones, unshaped boulders inscribed in Latin and in Roman capital letters, show there was a British Christian community in the South of Scotland in the 5th and 6th centuries AD. Little is known of these early Christians historically, but tradition names St Ninian as the missionary founder of the church at Whithorn in Galloway in the 5th century.

The gravestones are related to similar early monuments in Wales and Cornwall.

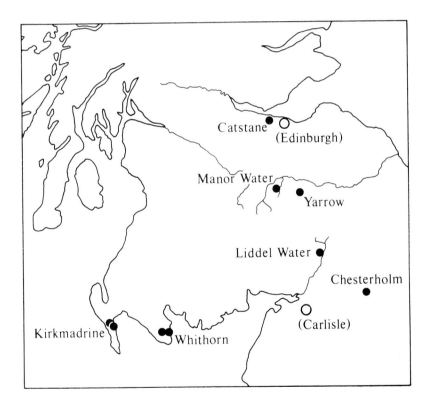

Early Christian gravestones of the 5th and 6th centuries AD in Scotland and Northern England (solid circles).

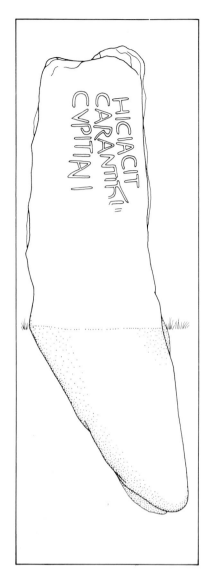

Liddel Water,
Roxburghshire
IB 240
Length 1.73 m

Gravestone with a Latin inscription commemorating a Christian Briton, found in 1933 in the bed of the Liddel Water, into which it had apparently fallen from a drystone dyke. This irregular slab would originally have been set upright, with the inscription reading vertically downwards, as in the drawing. The part of the stone that was in the ground is less weathered than the rest. The inscription reads:

HIC IACIT
CARANTI FIL(I)
CVPITIANI

'Here lies Carantus, son of Cupitianus.'

Both personal names are British, and are also known from monuments in Wales.

RCAHMS 1956, 34, 88–9.

ANGLIAN CROSSES

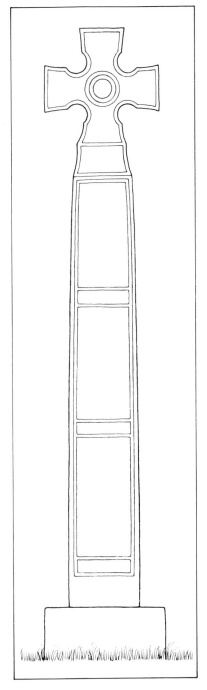

The Angles (English) captured the lands between the Forth and the Tweed from the Britons around AD 625–650. This area was then part of the Anglian kingdon of Northumbria for over three hundred years, until ceded to the Scots in 973. The Scottish conquest was finally confirmed by the Battle of Carham in 1018.

Among the few tangible remains of the period are a number of Anglian crosses. Decorative sculpture, figures and 'tree of life' vine-scroll patterns, had already been introduced into the churches built in the late 7th century for the monasteries of Northumbria by continental architects and masons. Yet it is believed that large free-standing stone crosses were unknown in early Christian art until devised in Northumbria in the 8th century AD, though there are earlier traditions of wooden crosses. The great stone cross at Ruthwell in Dumfriesshire and its neighbours at Bewcastle in Cumbria and Hexham in Northumberland form the beginning of the series, and may date to around 750. These were followed in the later 8th and 9th centuries by crosses such as those from Aberlady (p 16), Morham (p 17) and Hoddom (p 18), and those still at Abercorn, and by the shrine and crosses at Jedburgh. The tall shafts usually carried a small cross of four equal arms expanding at the ends and having a central disc symbolical of Christ's victory over death (in contrast to the later representation of the Crucified Christ); similar jewelled crosses were worn as pendants. A cross at Hoddom, now destroyed, had larger arms and Christ in Majesty sculptured in its central roundel. Such Anglian sculpture had a profound influence on Pictish sculpture north of the Forth.

Outline drawing of an Anglian cross.

Aberlady, East Lothian
IB 298
Height 0.61 m

Part of the shaft of an Anglian cross, found in 1863 built into the wall of the manse garden at Aberlady.

The broader faces are framed and divided into panels. On one face are four birds symmetrically arranged with their necks interwoven and their legs drawn out into interlaced strands; below this is part of a panel of diagonal key pattern. On the opposite side are a pair of reptilian beasts with their necks and limbs intertwined and below them a winged angel. Both narrow sides carry a simple vine scroll. The interlaced birds and beasts and the vine scrolls resemble those in late 7th–8th century manuscripts and on other Northumbrian sculpture, but angels usually appear with other figures, not alone.

Allen 1903, 428–9.

Morham, East Lothian
L.1928.6
Height 1.02 m

Part of the shaft of an Anglian cross. This was built into the outside wall of the parish church with only one face visible until 1928.

One of the broader faces has a vine scroll 'inhabited' by birds and beasts. These animals are typical of 9th century Anglian sculpture in Yorkshire. The other broad face has two different types of ribbon interlace, very accurately executed. The strands have a central incised line. The narrow sides have vine trails with small bunches of grapes and long leaves, and the angles are decorated with cable pattern.

Callander 1933, 241–3.

Hoddom, Dumfriesshire.
IB 9
Height 0.60 m

Part of the shaft of an Anglian cross, one of a group of fragmentary crosses found in the 19th century on the site of an assumed monastery.

On the front is a figure of Christ in classical dress holding a book, standing in front of a church. The gable cross, round-headed door and window, and the stepped capitals and bases to the door-frame are of Anglo-Saxon character. Above the roof are two attendant figures (sun and moon?). On the narrow sides are two very similar busts of saints or apostles holding books; there are buildings behind them. The blank spaces could have been intended for a painted inscription. The fourth side is now defaced, but has traces of two figures side by side.

Allen 1903, 439–40.

RINGED CROSSES

Early free-standing ringed crosses are found in Argyll, the original kingdom of the (Irish) Scots, at Kildalton and Iona from about AD 800, and in Ireland. Related ringed crosses are carved in relief on some major Pictish cross-slabs such as one at Aberlemno, Angus, and often on lesser ones, as Invergowrie (p 39). The ring is not found on contemporary Anglo-Saxon crosses or abroad, or on the earliest sculptures at Iona. It may have started as a device to support longer arms either for wooden crosses, or for stone crosses constructed with mortice-and-tenon joints in a carpentry technique as known at Iona. The idea must ultimately derive from the early wreath-encircled Christian symbols and the subsequent representations of crosses with central roundels.

Ringed and related disc-headed crosses are later found wide-spread in western Britain, and in the Anglo-Danish Kingdom of York which was similarly influenced by Ireland.

Kildalton, Islay
IB 6
Height 2.65 m

A cast of this cross is displayed in the National Museum. The illustrations show the original, still standing in Kildalton churchyard. This is the most perfect surviving example of a ringed cross in Scotland.

The large cross-head and the shaft are carved from a single block of stone. The front has complex decoration, including interlace, four animals in high relief, large bosses covered with close mesh patterns, and 'bird's nest' bosses (these have sunk centres with small bosses inside). Most of these are set against a background of twining serpents.

The back of the cross has figure subjects on the head, including the sacrifice of Isaac on the right arm and the Virgin and Child between two angels on the lower arm, also small bosses between twining snakes. The design on the shaft is composed of small bosses and spiral patterns very like those in the Book of Kells. The ring has also been decorated on both sides, though the patterns are now very worn.

Several features of the decoration link this cross with the crosses known as St John's and St Oran's Crosses on Iona, with the Pictish cross-slab at Nigg, Ross-shire and with the shrine at St Andrews, Fife. All these may date to around AD 800.

Allen 1903, 391–3.

20

PICTISH SYMBOL STONES

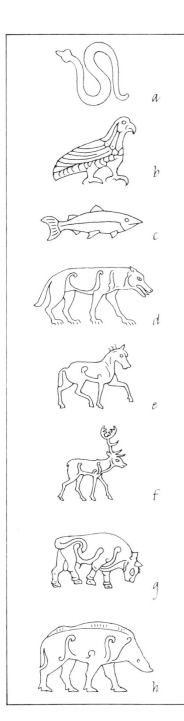

Nearly 200 stones incised with line drawings, and later cross-slabs carved with symbols in relief, show the Picts had a unique uniform system of symbols used throughout their kingdom, from Fife to Shetland. The linear symbols are incised on unworked stones, ranging from naturally shaped sandstone slabs, where available, to rough boulders. Most stones were specially erected, but some symbols may have been cut on pre-existing standing stones, for instance the symbol on a stone in the prehistoric circle at Broomend of Crichie, Aberdeenshire. The symbols also occur occasionally in caves and on rock surfaces.

Some symbols are recognisable, particularly the naturalistic animals, boar, bull, fish, goose, snake and deer, and familiar objects, such as the mirror and comb, or the tongs. A few apparently abstract designs may be simplified views of other objects; thus the three discs and bar is probably a cauldron seen from above. Other symbols may be purely abstract. The V-rod and Z-rod have been identified as a broken arrow and spear, but could as easily be sceptres or something quite different. Incised symbols are almost always found two to a stone, with the mirror and comb sometimes added probably to indicate a woman. The animal symbols are sometimes found alone, particularly around the Moray Firth.

Both the meaning of the symbols and the reason for the erection of the stones is unknown. At present a growing body of circumstantial evidence suggests the symbol stones were gravestones. If this was the case, the symbols might refer to the genealogy of the deceased, or perhaps to their position in society.

Evidence of style, particularly the close similarity between the Pictish animals and eagle and the symbols of the Evangelists in certain illuminated (painted) Gospel books, suggests that the Pictish symbols had begun by AD 700, though exactly how long before is arguable. Most incised symbol stones may date to the century from AD 685, with some carved later particularly in Aberdeenshire. That was a period when the Pictish kingdom was both strong and Christian, and when art in neighbouring Northumbria was having a 'Golden Age'. The symbols also occur on a few silver and other portable objects.

Pictish animal symbols: a, snake; b, eagle; c, fish; d, wolf; e, horse; f, stag; g, bull; h, boar.

a

b

c

d

e

f

g

h

i

j

Ogam Inscriptions

A few Pictish symbol stones, and rather more Pictish cross-slabs, have ogam inscriptions carved on them. These can be read but are generally unintelligible, and only a few words can be translated, usually personal names.

The ogam alphabet may have been invented in Ireland in the 4th century AD. Some 300 ogam inscriptions survive in Ireland, and others in Wales and Cornwall. These date mostly to the 5th and 7th centuries AD, and are memorials to persons with Celtic names. Only a few ogams in Scotland were cut across the corner angle of a stone in the Irish manner. One of these is on the island of Gigha, Argyll, while another was found at Poltalloch, also in Argyll.

Most of the two dozen or so ogam inscriptions in Scotland are Pictish, and date to the 8th and 9th centuries AD. They were written in a late form of the script, which among other changes used an incised base line instead of an angle of the stone, and some extra letters. Sometimes the ends of the letters were joined up by an extra line. These are known as 'bind ogams'.

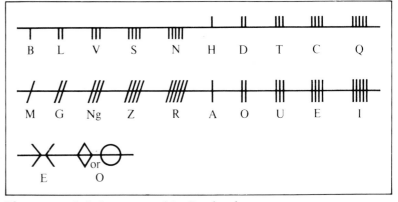

The ogam alphabet as used in Scotland.

Pictish symbols: a, mirror and comb; b, double-disc and Z-rod; c, crescent and V-rod; d, snake and Z-rod; e, notched-rectangle and Z-rod; f, rectangle; g, 'tuning-fork'; h, 'flower'; i, 'dog's head'; j, 'Pictish beast' or 'elephant'.

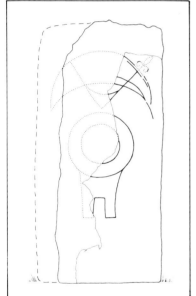

St Peter's Church,
South Ronaldsay, Orkney
IB 2
Height 1.50 m

This stone was built into St Peter's Church as a window sill until about 1852. There are symbols on both sides, and the stone has been used twice. On one side are a crescent and V-rod and a 'mirror-case', now partly flaked away. There seems to have been a deliberate attempt to deface the remaining portion of the symbols by pecking. On the other side are a rectangular symbol, possibly representing a book satchel, and a crescent and V-rod, both filled with curvilinear patterns.

Allen 1903, 20–1.

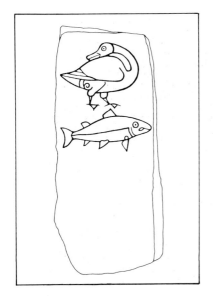

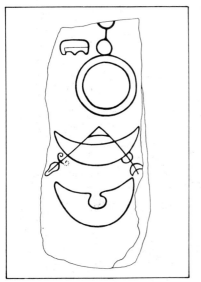

Easterton of Roseisle,
Morayshire
IB 226
Height 1.30 m

The stone was found in 1895 re-used as a wall slab in a cist-like structure, with the animal symbols hidden.

It had previously been used twice as a symbol stone. The earlier symbols are a crescent with a bite out of it, a crescent and V-rod, and a mirror and comb. The stone was later turned the other way up, the original symbols were partly defaced, and on the other side were carved a goose and a fish, probably a salmon. Several other symbol stones are known with evidence for the carving of successive groups of symbols.

Allen 1903, 124–6.
Stevenson 1959, 36.

24

Grantown, Morayshire
IB 10
Height 1.20 m

The stone was found around 1865 by a man digging into a knoll called Cnoc-an-Fruich.

This is a tall, narrow stone, roughly square in section, and has symbols finely incised on one face. At the top is a red deer stag with a fine head of antlers, below is a rectangle with spirals attached to two corners.

Allen 1903, 126–7.

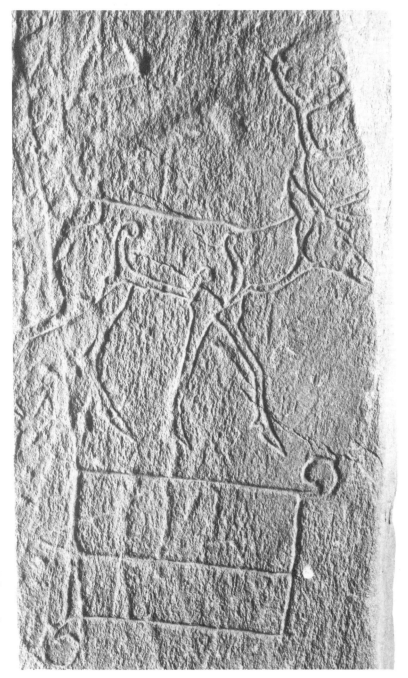

Burghead, Morayshire
IB 95
Height 0.69 m

Slab with a single bull symbol, said to have been found long ago in the well at Burghead.

At least five similar slabs have been found in the village, and they are now divided between Burghead and Elgin Museums and the British Museum. This is the only group of Pictish stones that repeat a single theme in one place. Three other slabs with single bulls are known, two found near Inverness and one in Fife, but these are feeble representations when compared to the powerful animals at Burghead.

Pictish animal symbols, otherwise naturalistic, have decorative scrolls defining the joints where the limbs join the body. The scrolls on the Burghead bulls are closely similar to those on St Luke's animal-symbol in a Northumbrian Gospel-book, known as the Echternach Gospels, of about AD 700 (there a calf rather than, as usually, a bull).

Allen 1903, 119.

26

Ackergill, Caithness
IB 168
Height 1.20 m

The slab has the remains of a fish symbol, most of which has flaked off, above a rectangle (perhaps a book satchel) filled with curvilinear patterns. To the left is an ogam inscription, which reads, from the bottom upwards, NEHTETRI . . ., the rest of the inscription being broken off. The beginning may be an abbreviated form of the name Nechton, known from Pictish historical sources.

This slab once stood at the end of a long mound near Ackergill Tower. Excavations in 1926 and 1927 revealed several long cist graves in rectangular cairns underneath the mound. The graves are probably Pictish, and this symbol stone, and a fragment of a second stone from the site, may have been associated with graves.

Allen 1903, 28–9.
Edwards 1926, 179.

Barflat, Rhynie,
Aberdeenshire
IB 307
Height 1.78 m

Cast of a symbol stone ploughed up in 1978. This stone is very unusual in having a single human figure occupying a large area of the stone. A man is shown standing facing right, wearing a short belted tunic with long sleeves. He has a moustache and beard, thick eyebrows, and either a head-dress or a strange hairstyle. He wields an axe, blade forward, with both hands.

Only two other stones with comparable incised single figures are known. One, found at Rhynie long ago, is now so weathered that no details of the figure can be made out. The other is a curious figure on a stone from Balblair, Inverness. However, closer similarity to the Rhynie man can be found on the Pictish relief monuments, particularly an incised figure on a cross-slab at Golspie, Sutherland, and the left-hand of two figures fighting with axes on another cross-slab at Glamis, Angus. There are various other figures in short tunics with beards and prominent noses, but the fierce grimace of the Rhynie man is so far unique. Perhaps he is a character from Pictish legend, rather than a symbol?

Shepherd and Shepherd 1978.

PICTISH CROSS-SLABS WITH SYMBOLS

Continued contact with classical art through the Roman church led the Picts to erect monumental crosses decorated in relief. The Anglo-Saxons in Northumbria, then including Lothian and the Borders, erected free-standing stone crosses from around AD 750. The relief sculpture of the Picts may derive from these crosses, or it may have begun earlier, under the influence of the late 7th – early 8th century Anglo-Saxon relief sculpture. However this may be, the Picts chose to have more space, by, as it were, transferring the cross-pages of gospel manuscripts on to large stone slabs. On the front of the slab they put the Cross, covered with interlace and cruciform patterns, and flanked by figures. On the back there was room for their own symbols, now more highly decorated but not so accurately drawn, and also Biblical and other illustrations. (The Pictish cross-slabs with symbols were called Class II by Romilly Allen, and the outline symbol stones Class I. These terms are used in many books.)

Interlace patterns, after being used by the Romans, were re-introduced into the British Isles from the Continent around AD 600 and they are found first in Anglo-Saxon metalwork. New forms had been devised in the East Mediterranean and among the Germanic peoples, but the complex 'knotting', which appears in Gospel manuscripts after 650, seem to have been an Insular development. Not peculiar to the Celts, it stimulated their fondness for intricacy. Often a negative cross-shape is formed between the curves of the interlace. The specifically Celtic contribution to the repertoire of Dark Age sculpture was the rich variety of curvilinear and spiral patterns which also figure earlier in manuscripts and on metalwork (cf. the basal panel of the Hilton of Cadboll stone, p 32).

The Pictish symbols began to die out after the Scots became rulers of Pictland (AD 843). Cross-slabs without symbols continued long in some areas (for instance at St Andrews, Fife), but art generally was impoverished, in part through wars with the Vikings.

Birsay, Orkney
IB 243
Height 1.87 m

Part of a large slab, now reassembled from fragments, found in 1935 during excavation of the graveyard of St Peter's Church on the Brough of Birsay. Contrary to earlier reports, it does not seem to have been associated with a triple grave.

The surviving pieces are only about one inch (25 mm) thick, and one side is lost. Presumably the missing side was sculptured with a cross.

On the surviving side are incised four symbols, the 'mirror-case', crescent and V-rod, Pictish beast and eagle. Below these, three warriors carved in low relief stand facing right; they are dressed in long tunics and carry spears, swords and square shields. On the shields are shown a square boss and the rivets that fastened the handle to the back. The warrior in front is distinguished by his curly hair, fringed tunic and decorated shield, and it may be that the slab was erected for him. The very low relief on this slab suggests it is transitional between the stones with incised symbols only and the cross-slabs with decoration in bold relief.

Curle 1982, 13–14, 97–100.
RCAHMS 1946, fig 57.

Dunfallandy, Perthshire
IB 53
Height above ground 1.46 m

Cast of a cross-slab still at Dun-fallandy. This cross-slab stood in 1856 in the ruins of an old chapel at Dunfallandy House (not, as Allen states, at Killie-crankie) and was later moved to Dunfallandy Cottage.

On the front is a cross decorated with a variety of motifs includ-ing interlace and small bosses with spirals, and surrounded by angels and fantastic beasts. The lowest beast on the left is prob-ably meant to be the whale swallowing Jonah, although it has front legs as well as a fish's tail.

On the back, which is bordered by two beasts with animal heads and fish tails, are two persons, perhaps clerics or saints, seated in chairs on either side of a small cross. Above them are three symbols, a Pictish beast, a double disc, and a crescent and V-rod, also an unfinished raised area where the sculptor may have intended to carve a fourth symbol. In a separate panel below is a man on horseback, with a crescent and V-rod, Pictish beast, hammer-and-anvil and a pair of tongs. The hammer-and-anvil is a rare symbol; its only other occurr-ence is on a symbol stone at Abernethy, Perthshire. It is possible that this symbol, like the mirror-and-comb, was a de-scriptive symbol added to the standard pair of symbols, and if so it probably signifies a smith.

Allen 1903, 286–9.
Henderson 1967, 147–8.

Hilton of Cadboll,
Ross-shire
IB 189
Height 2.34 m

The stone was first discovered about 1811 lying with its decorated face downwards in the graveyard of the small ruined chapel at Hilton of Cadboll. Sometime between 1856 and 1903 it was moved to the grounds of the Invergordon Castle, where it stood in the open and deteriorated rapidly. In 1921 it was sent to the British Museum but after protests was returned to Scotland.

The elaborate cross which once decorated the front of the stone was removed in the 17th century to make room for the following inscription:

VEIL
HE·THAT·LEIVES·VEIL·DOOES
SAYETH SOLOMON THE VYSE
HEIR LYES ALEXANDER DYF
AND HIS THREE WYVES 1676

A	DYF
K	S
C	V
H	V

In the event, it seems that this Alexander Duff was buried at the Abbey of Fearn, and this stone was never used as his gravestone.

The back of the stone is one of the most remarkable of Pictish monuments. The borders are filled with a bird-inhabited vine-scroll derived from Anglo-Saxon models, (see Morham, p 17). Within the frame are four panels. At the top are a double disc and Z-rod, a crescent and V-rod, and two discs, all highly decorated with spirals, key pattern, and 'knitted' interlace. Lower down is a scene with figures. A woman is riding side-saddle with her husband alongside her; not much can be seen of him except his face in profile and the legs of his horse. Her cloak is fastened by a penannular brooch. The mirror and comb symbols are prominently displayed to her left, suggesting that the slab was erected for her. On her right are trumpeters and a small lion, while below are two warriors with spears and shields, and a deer attacked by two hounds. Though apparently a hunting scene, this group incorporates elements from different sources; for instance the trumpeters and lion were probably derived from manuscript illustrations of David the Psalmist. The basal panel is filled with an elegant design of interlocking spirals, the lower half of which is lost.

Allen 1903, 61–3.
Stevenson 1959, 41–2.
Henderson 1967, 152–5.

Woodwrae, Angus
IB 202
Height 1.76 m

This cross-slab was found at the old castle of Woodwray in 1819, and was presented to Sir Walter Scott and erected on his estate at Abbotsford. It was moved from Abbotsford to the National Museum in 1923.

On the front there is a cross, which has been defaced, probably in the 17th century. It is surrounded by fantastic beasts, including a pair of interlaced snakes and a creature swallowing a man whose legs protrude from its mouth (compare a scene on the Dunfallandy cross-slab, p 31). The back has flaked badly, and only a few fragments remain. In a panel at the top is a man riding on a horse with the double disc and rectangle symbols displayed beside him; below is another rider and parts of several fantastic beasts. The bottom of the stone is missing.

Allen 1903, 242–5.

OTHER SCULPTURE

In this section only a small selection of the wide variety of later sculpture can be illustrated. Among the main groups of sculpture that should be represented here are Pictish monuments without symbols, such as cross-slabs, crosses, shrines and recumbent stones; the sculpture of southern Pictland after the union of Picts and Scots; early Scottish sculpture in Argyll, particularly at Iona; the late Norse-influenced cross-slabs of Galloway and the Clyde; the later sculpture of the far North; and the hogback tombstones of southern Scotland, of Anglo-Danish derivation.

Allen 1903.
Stevenson 1955, 1959 and 1981.

Papil, Isle of Burra,
Shetland
IB 46
Height 2.10 m

An unusual Pictish cross-slab found in 1877, lying on the ground near the churchyard of Papil. The slab is sculptured in low relief on one side only. Other sculptured stones (now in Lerwick Museum) have been found at Papil, where the name implies the site of of a monastery. (*Papa* is the Old Norse word for priest or monk.)

The curvilinear equal-armed cross in an arch at the top has four almond-shaped spaces filled with interlace. The form of the cross, with circular head and stem, probably derives from a ceremonial fan (*flabellum*). On either side of its small shaft stand two clerics with pointed hoods, having book satchels slung around their necks, and holding croziers. Below is a panel with a lion, similar in style to the Pictish animal symbols but here most probably representing the lion of St Mark. At the bottom are two figures with bird's legs and bird's beaks, carrying axes with T-shaped blades, and pecking at a human head between them. A natural flaw in the stone has influenced their position.

Allen 1903, 11.
Thomas 1971, 153–6; 1973, 29.

Bressay, Shetland
IB 109
Height 1.20 m

Cross-slab said to have been found at Culbinsgarth on the island of Bressay before 1859.

On one side is a cross with expanded arms within a circle. The cross and the spaces between its arms are all filled with interlace patterns. The top of the stone is framed by two monsters, swallowing a small human figure held between their jaws. Below the cross is a horseman, and to either side a hooded cleric with crozier and book satchel. Below the figures is a lion, and a smaller animal perhaps intended for a pig.

On the other side of the stone is an irregular circular cross composed of interlaced bands, and surrounded by a ribbon interlace incorporating generally late features such as strands which divide, and interlaced rings already seen on the Papil cross. Below this is a panel with two beasts, probably lions, facing each other with open mouths. At the bottom is a panel with two clerics, again with pointed hoods, croziers and book satchels.

On the sides are ogam inscriptions, which read, from the bottom upwards:

CRROSCC : NAHHTVVDDADDS : DATTRR : ANN
BENNISES : MEQQDDRROANN

This stone is thought to be a 9th or 10th century copy of the Papil stone (p 34). Three words can be recognised; crroscc (cross) and meqq (of the son of) are Gaelic words, while dattr is the Norse word for daughter. The other words appear to be Pictish. The use of two dots as punctuation between words has been borrowed from Norse runic inscriptions, while doubled consonants are found in Irish ogams. The whole suggests that a Christian community speaking a very mixed language continued in Shetland after the Norse settlement.

Allen 1903, 5–10.
Jackson 1955, 140–2.

St Andrews, Fife
IB 13–15
Width of central panel, 1.06 m

Casts of the remains of a Pictish composite stone shrine are exhibited in the National Museum. The originals have been reconstructed in the museum at St Andrews Cathedral, where they were discovered in 1833 about 6 feet underground near St Rule's Tower.

The major surviving pieces of the shrine are two corner posts, one front panel, and an end panel. These form part of a decorated box-like shrine, the panels having projecting tongues which fit into slots in the corner posts. No part of the lid has survived and it may have been flat, though at St Andrews it has been restored as a steeply pitched roof. The shrine would have stood inside a church and may have contained a wooden reliquary-box with the relics of a saint, perhaps St Rule or St Andrew.

The front panel is decorated in high relief with a series of scenes derived ultimately from late classical sources; on the right is David rending the jaws of the lion; in the centre, David on horseback with a falcon defends his sheep from a lion; to the left are hunting scenes. This central panel is flanked by groups of writhing interlaced snake-like animals on the front of the end posts. The sides of the posts, and the end panel, are covered with a close mesh interlace that includes small sunk crosses. Round the large square cross on the end panel, with its central

The shrine as displayed at St Andrews; only the sculptured panels are original.

boss decorated with small spirals, are sunk panels containing two bosses with snakes twined around them and two pairs of monkeys.

The figures on the front of the shrine, particularly the large figure of David with his draped clothing, the trees and foliage on the left, the griffin attacking a mule, and the monkeys on the end panel, are among the closest copies of southern art to be found in Pictland, and are thus of the utmost importance for the chronology of relief monuments. Origins have been seen for various elements of the design in manuscripts, in Byzantine ivories, in the

Anglo-Saxon relief sculpture of Mercia, and the Rothbury cross in Northumberland, all objects dating at latest to around 800. A date for the St Andrews shrine at the beginning of the 9th century may be suggested.

Closely related to the St Andrews shrine by elements of their decoration, particularly the large bosses entwined by snakes in relief, are the Pictish cross-slab at Nigg and the Scotic crosses at Iona and Kildalton.

Composite stone shrines are rather unusual dark age monuments, but they seem to be one of a number of native efforts to reproduce the shape of a classical sarcophagus (stone coffin). Among the other instances in Scotland are parts of an Anglian stone shrine at Jedburgh, parts of cruder Pictish composite shrines from Papil and St Ninian's Isle in Shetland, and from Burghead, and parts of shrines, of which mostly only end posts survive, from Iona. All of these were probably associated with monasteries.

Allen 1903, 350–3, no 1.
Curle 1940, 98–100.
Stevenson 1955, 117–9.
Radford 1955.
Henderson 1967, 149–152.
Thomas 1971, 148–163.

Cast of the side of the shrine.

Murthly, Perthshire
IB 101
Length 1.13 m

A slab decorated on one side with a series of fantastic creatures. It was ploughed up at Gellyburn in 1886. No evidence survives as to how this slab was used. It has been suggested it may have been a side panel from a Pictish composite stone shrine somewhat similar to those of which parts have been found at Papil and St Ninian's Isle, Shetland, and related to the elaborate composite shrine from St Andrews, Fife.

On the left, two figures with human bodies but bird or beast heads are fighting with sword and shield. In the centre are a pair of sea monsters. On the right a small human figure is pursued by a predatory beast, while below is a creature with a long snout, goggle eyes, forelegs and a fish's tail. The slab may date to the mid 9th century.

Allen 1903, 305–6.

Bullion, Invergowrie,
Angus
IB 229
Height 1.88 m

This unusual slab was discovered in 1934 when the Kings-
way extension was constructed
round Dundee. It is decorated in
relief on one side only. A
horseman, his round shield
slung across his shoulders,
drinks from a horn held in his
right hand, while the horse
plods uphill. The bird head on
the drinking horn is twisted to
look down on the rider.

There is no strictly comparable
monument in Pictland or indeed
elsewhere. It may be the work of
an unusually imaginative local
sculptor of the first half of the
10th century.

Stevenson 1959, 43–5.

Invergowrie, Angus
IB 251
Height 0.84 m

A cross-slab without symbols, perhaps dating to the late 9th century. It was for many years built into a window opening of the old ruined church.

On the front is a ringed cross filled with interlace, and four panels of key pattern in the corners of the slab. On the back is a panel of three clerics (?) holding books, the central figure also holding some unidentified object. The two outer figures have curious discs with crosses on their shoulders, sometimes said to be brooches, but perhaps part of the decoration of their vestments. Below are two dragonlike beasts, biting each other's tails with their fangs, and having curly manes the length of their bodies. Their double outline is characteristic of the Anglo-Danish sculpture of England. The top edge of the slab is decorated with key pattern and the sides with interlace.

Allen 1903, 255–6.

Forteviot, Perthshire
IB 36
Width 1.92 m

Part of an arch from the top of a large doorway. It was found before 1832 in the Water of May, below Holy Hill at the west end of the village.

The arch is a substantial stone, 38 cm thick. The back was left undressed and was concealed in the thickness of the wall. The front is carved in relief with a number of figures. In the centre is a cross, now defaced, and beside it an animal probably intended to be a lamb. To the right of this are two men with long moustaches, wrapped in hooded cloaks and holding staves in their hands. The man at the right is sitting down with his legs bent up. On the other side is a single sitting figure with a long moustache and curly hair, holding a staff or sword across his knees. Below his feet is a small animal, probably an ox. The perspective is curious, but the attitude which the sculptor was trying to depict is shown in a later context by the kings among the 12th century Norse chessmen from Lewis, seated on chairs and grasping with both hands swords in scabbards laid across their knees.

The arch must have come from a substantial stone building. It framed an opening at least 1.20 m wide, and was probably the top of a large doorway, perhaps of a church porch. Forteviot in the 9th century AD was the site of a Pictish royal residence, afterwards used by the Scottish kings. According to some sources, the last king of the Picts was killed at Forteviot, and Kenneth MacAlpine, the first king of the united kingdom of Picts and Scots, died there. The sculpture of the arch is thought to date to the late 9th or 10th century, so it could belong to a church built by one of the Scottish kings who succeeded Kenneth.

The sculpture on this arch is related to the cross at Dupplin in Perthshire, particularly the figures shown in profile with the same long moustaches, and to the Invergowrie and Benvie cross-slabs. The sculptors of these monuments, though technically Scots, were still working in a Pictish tradition. For instance, the remains of the joint scrolls first seen on the earlier Pictish animal symbols still appear on the arch, on the lamb beside the cross.

Allen 1903, 324–5.
Henderson 1978, 56–7.

Glenluce, Wigtownshire
IB 45
Height 1.70 m

This cross-slab, dug up in the churchyard of Glenluce some time in the 19th century, was used for many years as a seat at the door of a house in the village.

It is decorated on one side only. At the top is a cross of 'Maltese' shape, with four low bosses in the angles of the arms. Below this on the shaft is a long panel of interlace incorporating loose rings, with a small strip of tighter interlace at the bottom.

This slab is related to a group of 10th and 11th century crosses, most having wheel or disc-shaped heads, which are found in Galloway, an area then having strong Irish-Norse connections. They resemble other groups of late crosses in Cumbria, Wales and Cornwall.

Allen 1903, 482.
Stevenson 1956, map on page 124.

NORSE CROSS-SLABS

Although many pagan Norse graves are known, especially from the Northern and Western Isles, only a few scattered Norse Christian gravestones are known there. Among them are the Bressay stone (p 35), part of a slab at Jarlshof, also in Shetland, a cross-shaped stone from Thurso, a gravestone at Iona, and the two cross-slabs illustrated here.

Norse Runic Inscriptions

Norse runes differ from the runes used earlier by the Anglo-Saxons, of which a few examples are known from Scotland, notably on the Ruthwell cross. There are several versions of the ordinary runic alphabet, besides others more cryptic; all may have had magical as well as religious uses.

The earliest Norse runic inscriptions in Scotland are gravestones, some carved only with runes, of the 10th and 11th centuries AD (p 43). Later runic inscriptions include the important group of thirty in the neolithic chambered tomb of Maes Howe, Orkney, which date to the 12th century. Two there tell of Crusaders, 'Jerusalem men', breaking into the Howe; these may relate to the expedition of Earl Rognvald and Eindrid the Younger which wintered in Orkney in 1150–1 on their way to the Holy Land. The *Orkneyinga Saga* says of this winter: 'There was a great turmoil in the Islands; the Orkneymen and the Norwegians quarrelled frequently about bargains, and women, and other things. The Earl had a very difficult task to keep peace among them.' Several of the inscriptions in Maes Howe mention women; one reads 'Ingigerth is the fairest of women'. There are also runic inscriptions in St Molaise Cave on Holy Island, Arran, carved by members of King Haakon's expedition when his fleet lay in Lamlash Bay shortly before the battle of Largs in 1263.

Kilbar, Barra
IB 102
Height 1.65 m

The cross-slab was recognised in 1865 in the disused burial ground of the ruined church of Kilbar, on the island of Barra, in the Outer Hebrides.

On the front is a cross filled with rather irregular interlace formed from four bands. The top is damaged. On either side of the shaft are S-scrolls and key pattern.

On the back is a runic inscription, set out in two lines reading vertically downwards. Translated literally, this reads, 'after Thorgerth, Steinar's daughter, this cross was raised'; which may be expressed more freely as 'this cross was raised in memory of Thorgerth, daughter of Steinar'. The cross-slab dates to the 10th or early 11th century.

Allen 1903, 114–5.

Doid Mhairi, Port Ellen, Islay
IB 196
Height 1 m

Cross-slab found at Doid Mhairi, ('Mary's Croft'), near Port Ellen on the island of Islay in about 1838. It is decorated on one side only. The cross has a small ring round it, arms of rather irregular shape and a long shaft. Above the cross are two discs, probably intended to represent the sun and the moon. On each side of the shaft, and below it, is an irregular ribbon interlace, with foliage terminals in a local version of Norse 'Ringerike' style.

The slab was probably erected by a Christian Norseman in the 11th century AD.

Allen 1903, 379.
Stevenson 1959, 53–4.

REFERENCES

Allen, J R 1903 *The Early Christian Monuments of Scotland,* part III, Edinburgh.

Callander, J C 1933 A short cist containing a beaker at Newlands, Oyne, Aberdeenshire and sundry archaeological notes, *Proc Soc Antiq Scot* 67, 1932–3, 228–243.

Curle, C L 1940 The Chronology of the Early Christian Monuments of Scotland, *Proc Soc Antiq Scot* 74, 1939–40, 60–115.

Curle, C L 1982 *Pictish and Norse Finds from the Brough of Birsay, 1934–1974.*

Edwards, A J H 1926 Excavation of a number of graves in a mound at Ackergill, Caithness, *Proc Soc Antiq Scot* 60, 1925–6, 160–179.

Henderson, I 1978 Sculpture north of the Forth after the takeover by the Scots, in J Lang *ed, Early Anglo-Saxon and Viking Age Sculpture,* Oxford, 1978, 47–74.

Radford, C A R 1955 Two Scottish shrines: Jedburgh and St Andrews, *Archaeol Journal* 112, 1955, 43–60.

RCAHMS 1946 Royal Commission on the Ancient and Historical Monuments of Scotland, *Inventory of the Ancient Monuments of Orkney and Shetland,* Edinburgh, 1946.

RCAHMS 1956 Royal Commission on the Ancient and Historical Monuments of Scotland, *Inventory of Monuments in Roxburghshire,* Edinburgh, 1956.

Shepherd, I A G and Shepherd, A N 1978 An incised Pictish figure and a new symbol stone from Barflat, Rhynie, Gordon District, *Proc Soc Antiq Scot* 109, 1977–8, 211–222.

Stevenson, R B K 1955 Pictish Art, in Wainwright, F T *ed, The Problem of the Picts*, Edinburgh, 1955.

Stevenson, R B K 1956 The chronology and relationships of some Irish and Scottish crosses, *Journal Royal Soc Antiq Ireland* 86, 1956, 84–96.

Stevenson, R B K 1959 The Inchyra stone and some other unpublished Early Christian Monuments, *Proc Soc Antiq Scot* 92, 1958–9, 33–55.

Thomas, C 1971 *The Early Christian Archaeology of North Britain,* London, 1971.

SUGGESTIONS FOR FURTHER READING

J R Allen and J Anderson, *Early Christian Monuments of Scotland*, Edinburgh, 1903.

S Cruden, *The Early Christian and Pictish Monuments of Scotland*, Edinburgh, 1964.

W G Collingwood, *Northumbrian Crosses of the Pre-Norman Age*, London, 1927.

R B K Stevenson, Pictish Art in *The Problem of the Picts, ed* F T Wainwright, Edinburgh, 1955; new edition Perth 1980 (with supplementary bibliography 1954–1980).

Isabel Henderson, *The Picts*, London, 1967.

Isabel Henderson, The Meaning of the Pictish Symbol Stones in *The Dark Ages in the Highlands*, Inverness Field Club, 1971, 53–68.

G and A Ritchie, *Scotland: Archaeology and Early History*, London, 1981.

For children:–

Anna Ritchie, *The Kingdom of the Picts*, Edinburgh, 1977.

VISITS TO OTHER MONUMENTS

Many sculptured stones can be seen around Scotland, in or near their original position or in local museums. Information about these can be found in the books above and in various guidebooks, including the following:–

Scotland. Illustrated Guide to Ancient Monuments in the care of the Scottish Development Department (HMSO).

R Feachem, *A Guide to Prehistoric Scotland*, 1963; new ed. 1977.

E W MacKie, *Scotland, An Archaeological Guide*, 1975.

Ian A G Shepherd and Ian B M Ralston, *Early Grampian, A Guide to the Archaeology*, Aberdeen, 1979.

H Coutts, *The Ancient Monuments of Tayside*, Dundee Museum, 1970.

Particularly important collections of Dark Age sculptured monuments can be seen in:

St Andrew's Cathedral Museum, Fife (SDD)
Dundee Museum, Angus
Dunrobin Castle Museum, Sutherland
Elgin Museum, Morayshire
Govan church and churchyard, Glasgow
Inverness Museum
Meigle Museum, Perthshire (SDD)
St Vigeans Museum, Angus (SDD)
Whithorn Priory Museum, Wigtownshire (SDD)

SDD: monuments in the care of the Scottish Development Department, (see the first guide book listed above). At the time of writing in 1982 the opening hours of these monuments are erratic; it is best to check first with the Inspectorate of Ancient Monuments at 3–11 Melville Street, Edinburgh.

Her Majesty's Stationery Office

Government Bookshops

71 Lothian Road, Edinburgh EH3 9AZ
49 High Holborn, London WCV1V 6HB
9-21 Princes Street, Manchester M60 8AS
Southey House, Wine Street, Bristol BS1 2BQ
258 Broad Street, Birmingham B1 2HE
80 Chichester Street, Belfast BT1 4JY

*Government publications are also available
through booksellers*

Printed in Scotland for HMSO   Dd 0287336   C10   7/89   (22926)